PLAY BALL!

PLAY BALL!

An All-Star Lineup
of Baseball Cartoons

EDITED BY

S. Gross
and Jim Charlton

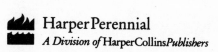
HarperPerennial
A Division of HarperCollins*Publishers*

Some of the cartoons in this collection have appeared in the following periodi-
cals and publications and are reprinted by permission of the authors: *Argosy,
Esquire, Fireside Book of Baseball 1987, Look, Saturday Evening Post, Sports
Illustrated.*

Cartoons copyrighted by *The New Yorker* are indicated throughout the book.

FIRST EDITION

Designed by Hudson Studio

LIBRARY OF CONGRESS CATALOG CARD NUMBER 90-50458

ISBN 0-06-096598-3

91 92 93 94 95   RRD   10 9 8 7 6 5 4 3 2 1

LEO CULLUM

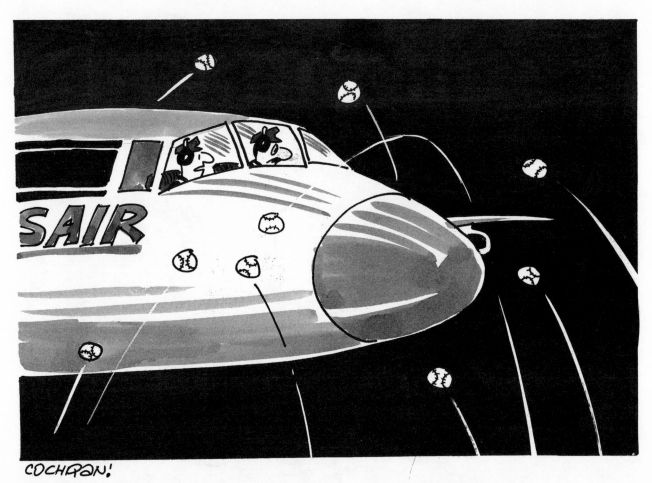

COCHRAN!

BRUCE COCHRAN

"So what do you think? Are the balls livelier this year?"

"It's the Hall of Fame if he ever learns to get that one over."

BRIAN SAVAGE

BASEBALL
PROMOTIONS
INC

"Bat Day seems like a good idea,
but I question the advisability of giving bats
in the Bronx to 40,000 Yankee fans."

AARON BACALL

HISTORY OF BASEBALL

1875

1900

1925

1950

1975

1990

ZIEGLER

JACK ZIEGLER

"I didn't get into college 'cause I had a high SAT. I got in 'cause I had a low ERA."

DAVE CARPENTER

SIPRESS

DAVID SIPRESS

THE HOUSE THAT RUTH REALLY BUILT.

OLIVER CHRISTIANSON

"How do you like that guy? Tossing me out for kicking a little dirt on him!"

JOHN ALBANO

"Because you slid
into the pitcher's mound,
that's why the commissioner
is ordering you to submit
to a drug test."

A. BACALL

AARON BACALL

THOMAS RUNYON

"Call the Kansas City Royals, Ma. The boy's ready."

"Hey! I said <u>NO PEPPER</u>!!!"

JOHN CALDWELL

ORLANDO BUSINO

"Today's session will be devoted to the restaurant franchise business."

"Well, it's a baseball movie, but it's not <u>about</u> baseball."

D. Barstow

D.L. BARSTOW

DANIEL COLLINS

"The only thing I can figure is that the Indians are in the Series."

STUART LEEDS

"Walter, why don't you tell these nice young gentlemen about those wonderful afternoons
at the Polo Grounds watching Carl Hubbell."

A DECLINING FRANCHISE

WEAK HITTING

FEW FANS

WARM BEER

SIDNEY HARRIS

FREE
AGENT

BERNARD SCHOENBAUM

"The general manager's wife picked out the artificial turf."

DON OREHEK

NEW INDUCTEES

CHARLES LEROY BUMPUS
"BUMP"
DETROIT, A.L., 1961-1975
LEADS ALL CATCHERS IN TRIPS TO THE
MOUND, 5091. LED A.L. IN FEWEST MEN-
TAL ERRORS 6 YEARS. LED MAJORS
TWICE IN NUMBER OF WAYS HE CAN HURT
YOU (INCLUDES PINCHING, BITING, CLAWING,
KICKING, AND VARIOUS ABUSES TO MOTOR
VEHICLES). 4-TIME GOLD TONGUE AWARD
FOR FLAWLESS POST-GAME DICTION.

DARRYL HUTCHINS STILLPASS
"THE GUY"
CHICAGO, N.L., 1955-1969
HOLDS MANY N.L. RECORDS. AMONG
THEM: OUT-OF-PLAY BALLS TOSSED TO
SCREAMING FANS, 3012; DOUBLE-PUMPS
ON THROWS FROM RIGHT FIELD, 1619;
UNNECESSARY SLIDES, 3006. PIONEERED
USE OF AIR BAG TO REDUCE RISK
OF INJURY IN OUTFIELD COLLISIONS.

LAWRENCE MUTZ FOYLE
"MOP"
CINCINNATI, N.L., 1963-1978
LED N.L. IN BOO-INCURRING PICKOFF
ATTEMPTS 4 YEARS; FIRST MODERN
LEFT-HAND "SHORT MAN" TO LOWER
PANTLEG BELOW CALF. N.L. CAREER LEADER
IN SIGNS SHAKEN OFF, 6327. HOLDS
WORLD SERIES RECORD FOR MOST
APPEARANCES WITHOUT USING
RESIN BAG, 17.

BENJAMIN TODD BARNES
"B.T."

BALTIMORE, A.L., 1957-1974
ALL-TIME MAJOR-LEAGUE LEADER
IN MOST ROUTINE POP-UPS TURNED
INTO ADVENTURES, 2781. FIRST A.L.
PLAYER TO ADJUST CAP PRIOR TO
BATTING. LED LEAGUE TWICE IN
FALSE STARTS TO FIRST BASE AFTER
ASSUMING BALL FOUR. MOST
AMUSING A.L. PLAYER IN 1970.

CRAWFORD

MICHAEL CRAWFORD

© 1989 The New Yorker Magazine, Inc.

I'M TAKING YOUR DAUGHTER OUT TO THE BALLGAME. I'M TAKING HER OUT TO THE CROWD. I'LL BUY HER SOME PEANUTS AND CRACKERJACKS

I DON'T CARE IF YOU NEVER GET BACK

A. BACALL

BASEBALL BONDING

AARON BACALL

STUART LEEDS

BRUCE COCHRAN

"These old ball parks have a charm all their own, don't they?"

"Gentlemen, another three-run homer by the Strawman!"

"We could be in Florida right now — but no, you've got to be a holdout!"

JERRY MARCUS

PETER MUELLER

BRUCE COCHRAN

"We need to win tomorrow's game,
Bobby, so I want you to make believe you're dying
of a rare disease so that Kirk will hit a home run for you."

MARK HEATH

JOHN DEMPSEY

"And how are the good old Boston Braves doing?"

MORT GERBERG

Bobby Thomson, at yet one more dinner, waits in vain for a question about his famous
home run that he hasn't heard before.

BORIS DRUCKER

"He got his first intentional walk today!"

JERRY MARCUS

BASEBALL EXECUTIVES CARDS

LAWRENCE (LAWRENCE) DOTRELL
HT.: 5'10"   WT.: 184
NET WORTH: $462,000,000

T	F	D	C	G	EG	M	I
4	1	6	4	9	0	3	2
1	0	3	6	10	1	4	1
7	2	3	6	12	1	4	3

1988
1989
1990

T. Threat to move team
F. Fired good manager
D. Dumb trades
C. Criticized team publicly

G. Grabbed headlines
EG. Failed to grab headlines
M. Minimized profits
I. Involved in collusion

SIDNEY HARRIS

ELDON DEDINI

"He's nervous as a cat. His babysitter's in the stands."

BERNARD SCHOENBAUM

"I was thrown out of the game, the stadium, the Series and baseball."

BORIS DRUCKER

JERRY MARCUS

"Where the hell is Wilcox?"

STUART LEEDS

"I love when you tell me why the designated hitter dilutes and distorts the spirit of the game and why the National League is courageous and forthright in not going into it."

"Hi, honey! I've rounded third and I'm home!"

HENRY MARTIN

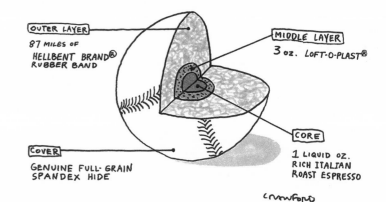

WHY THE BALL IS JUMPING OUT

OUTER LAYER
87 MILES OF
HELLBENT BRAND®
RUBBER BAND

MIDDLE LAYER
3 OZ. LOFT-O-PLAST®

CORE
1 LIQUID OZ.
RICH ITALIAN
ROAST ESPRESSO

COVER
GENUINE FULL-GRAIN
SPANDEX HIDE

MICHAEL CRAWFORD

"These seats are terrific."

V. GENE MYERS

''Mirror, mirror on the wall,
 who's the fairest of them all?''

SAM GROSS

"He says he can't come in to pitch the ninth inning, Skip. He's trying to finish the last chapter of his book."

MARTY MURPHY

"They're called 'the Southern Lights,' son. They began when night games came to Wrigley Field."

H.L. SCHWADRON

ARNIE LEVIN

AL ROSS

DANNY SHANAHAN

THOMAS RUNYON

"Elmer made his money in baseball. He saved his gum cards as a boy."

ARNIE LEVIN

"Yo, pal! Hot dogs! Sodas! Beer!"

JACK ZIEGLER

MUSEUM
OF
BROKEN
AND
CORKED
BATS

AL ROSS

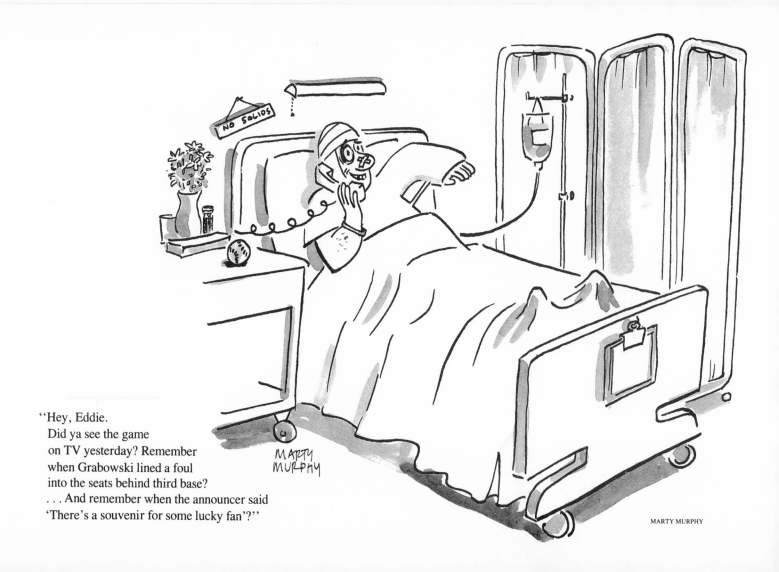

"Hey, Eddie.
  Did ya see the game
  on TV yesterday? Remember
  when Grabowski lined a foul
  into the seats behind third base?
  . . . And remember when the announcer said
  'There's a souvenir for some lucky fan'?''

MARTY MURPHY

"That's gonna be a balk every time, Mittens."

DANNY SHANAHAN

THE PINE TAR INCIDENT BAR & GRILL

ED FRASCINO

"First the good news, Fred —
they're retiring your number."

NICK DOWNES

"Sneakiest pick-off move in the American League."

VAHAN SHIRVANIAN

JOE MIRACHI

© 1984 The New Yorker Magazine, Inc.

"All right, men, this is it. There is no tomorrow."

"To the baths!"

SAUERS

CHARLES SAUERS

THE TEAM PHOTO

"The baseball strike made her smile."

ED FRASCINO

JOSEPH FARRIS

"Pro certo, Frater Benjamin,
tibi necesse est habere nova eyeglasses."

JOE MIRACHI

Lefty Duke Signs for a van Gogh Painting

Hard-hitting outfielder K.T. (Lefty) Duke signed a four-year contract with the Baltimore Orioles for which he will receive van Gogh's painting "The Crooked Road."

This contract exceeds that of Bananas Rohak, who signed yesterday for three years. Rohak will receive an early-nineteenth-century Regency desk. If he hits over .290, he will get the matching chair.

Duke hit .287 last season. Van Gogh painted "The Crooked Road" in 1884, and was unable to sell it in his lifetime. It was most recently owned by a private collector in Caracas.

SIDNEY HARRIS

"Computer error."

ARNIE LEVIN

"What these cherry blossoms say is that it's 'Play ball!'
at Korakuen Stadium and I'm not there."

EVERETT OPIE
© 1968 The New Yorker Magazine, Inc.

WORLD SERIES ACTION

WAITING FOR THE TV COMMERCIAL TO END

Drucker

BORIS DRUCKER

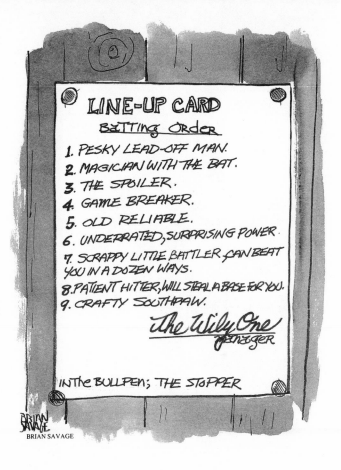

LINE-UP CARD
Batting Order

1. PESKY LEAD-OFF MAN.
2. MAGICIAN WITH THE BAT.
3. THE SPOILER.
4. GAME BREAKER.
5. OLD RELIABLE.
6. UNDERRATED, SURPRISING POWER.
7. SCRAPPY LITTLE BATTLER, CAN BEAT YOU IN A DOZEN WAYS.
8. PATIENT HITTER, WILL STEAL A BASE FOR YOU.
9. CRAFTY SOUTHPAW.

The Wily One
Manager

IN THE BULLPEN; THE STOPPER

BRIAN SAVAGE

ZIM   ZIMMER   ZIMMEST

JOHN CALDWELL

"We borrowed the idea from the Astrodome. It goes off every time
somebody hits a home run."

"His last words were 'Let's go Mets.'"

BRIAN SAVAGE

"We live in troubled times, McCarthy!"

SIDNEY HARRIS

"Son, are you familiar with the word 'obsession'?"

DAVID SIPRESS

IN THE WINTERTIME WHEN WE RURAL TYPES GATHER
'ROUND THE POTBELLIED STOVE FOR SOME BASEBALL BLATHER,
ONE SEARING QUESTION INFLAMES OUR TALK;
JUST WHAT IN **HELL** CONSTITUTES A 'BALK'?

BRIAN SAVAGE

"Going to throw out the first arm of the season?"

"Don't forget."

ELDON DEDINI

"Do you mind? I put on a few pounds over the winter, too."

VAHAN SHIRVANIAN

Philrizzuto Phunnies

JACK ZIEGLER

"On the other hand, there are some distinct advantages in having your team
continually in the cellar."

SIDNEY HARRIS

© 1989 The New Yorker Magazine, Inc.

"They're really getting to you.
Haven't you got anything besides
a fast ball, a curve, a sinker,
a knuckle ball, a change up,
a split finger, a forkball
and a screw ball?"

ANDY WYATT

"That's the first time a left-handed batter with a sub .300 average, batting as a pinch hitter in a blue uniform on a Thursday, ever hit a single off a right-handed pitcher with an above 2.51 E.R.A. weighing more than 165 pounds in an odd-numbered inning."

KEN WILKIE

POP-UP BOOKS

MARK HEATH

"The last time I saw them?
We were due to bat
in the bottom of the first,
trailing 19 to 0."

FRED THOMAS

VAHAN SHIRVANIAN

BORIS DRUCKER

"General Doubleday, sir, you're out."

"Good grief! I thought they settled all that nonsense last year."

PHIL INTERLANDI

ARNIE LEVIN

"Hey. I forgot what we decided on!"

"You can have the boys of summer!"

PETER PORGES

"Baseball start yet?"

Druker

BORIS DRUCKER

GEORGE JARTOS

"Mrs. Schott requests that you stop spitting during the close-ups."

JACK ZIEGLER

"If he'd ever connected the ball would still be traveling."

VAHAN SHIRVANIAN

"These are Reggie's favorite trophies — his product endorsement contracts."

CHARLES ALMON

BANNED PITCHES

THE BLACKENED CAJUNBALL

THE HI-TECH LASERBALL

THE LAKE MICHIGAN SKIPBALL

JACK ZIEGLER

DICK OLDDEN

"Yogi Berra says it's over."

ARNIE LEVIN